ROBBIE WILLIAMS

TAKE THE CROWN

© 2012 by Faber Music Ltd

First published by Faber Music Ltd in 2012

Bloomsbury House

74–77 Great Russell Street

London WC1B 3DA

Music Arranged by Olly Weeks

Edited by Lucy Holliday

Book Design by Chloë Alexander

Original album design by Tom Hingston Studio

Printed in England by Caligraving Ltd

This paper is 100% recyclable

ISBN10: 0-571-53742-1

EAN13: 978-0-571-53742-6

To buy Faber Music publications or to find out about the full range of titles available,
please contact your local music retailer or Faber Music sales enquiries:

Faber Music Limited, Burnt Mill, Elizabeth Way, Harlow CM20 2HX

Tel: +44 (0)1279 82 89 82

Fax: +44 (0)1279 82 89 83

sales@fabermusic.com

fabermusic.com

Contents

BE A BOY

Words and Music by Robbie Williams, Tim Metcalfe and Flynn Francis

(Oh, way,_____ oh, way,_____ oh, way,_____ oh, way.)_____

All the boys_ that could have been some - one, your time did come but now it's gone,_ your

time did come but now it's gone, it takes a big man to be some - one. takes a big man to be some - one. I'm

half your age_ and lived twice your life_ and I own the streets you walk to - night, the time did come but now it's gone, it

takes a big man to be some - one, I'm half your age___ and lived twice your life___ and

I don't sleep a - lone at night. The time did come but it's long gone, it takes a big man to be some - one.

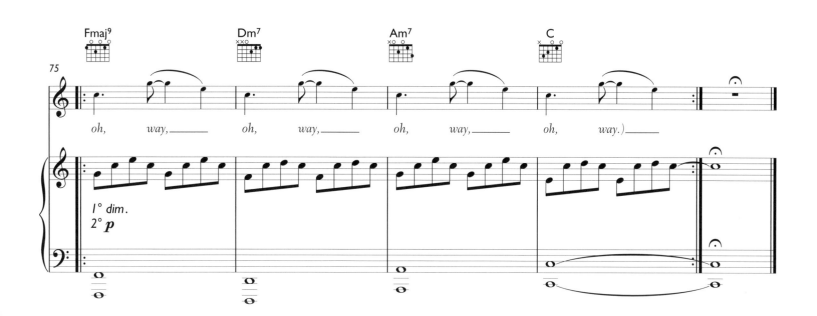

oh, way,_____ oh, way,_____ oh, way,_____ oh, way.)_____

GOSPEL

Words and Music by Robbie Williams, Tim Metcalfe, Flynn Francis and Jacknife Lee

1. I used to think a-bout it when I was a lit-tle one all a-lone, used to be so ex-

-cit - ed, so ex-cit - ed on my own.

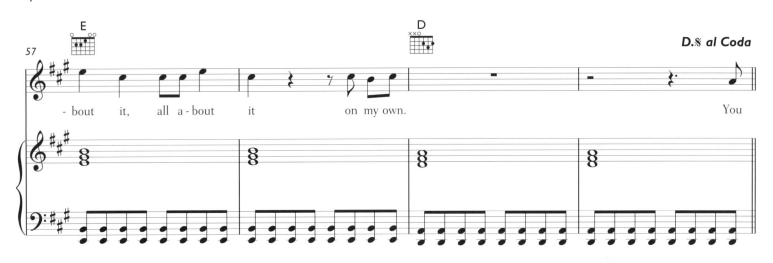

D.%. al Coda

-bout it, all a-bout it on my own. You

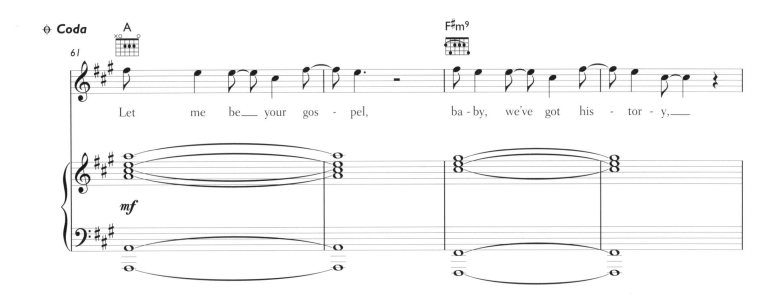

Let me be__ your gos - pel, ba - by, we've got his - tor - y,__

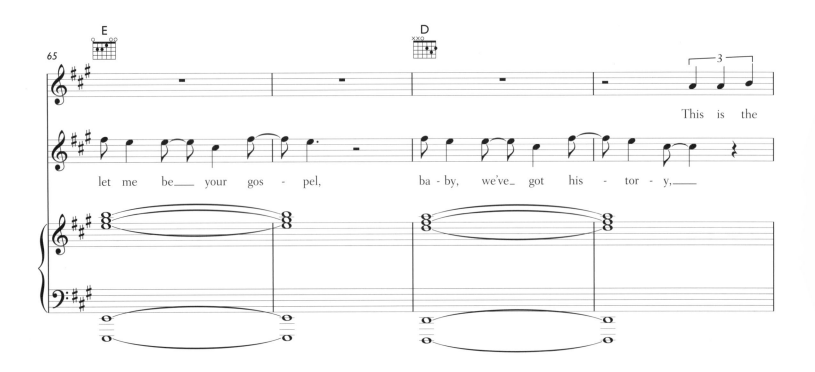

This is the

let me be__ your gos - pel, ba - by, we've__ got his - tor - y,__

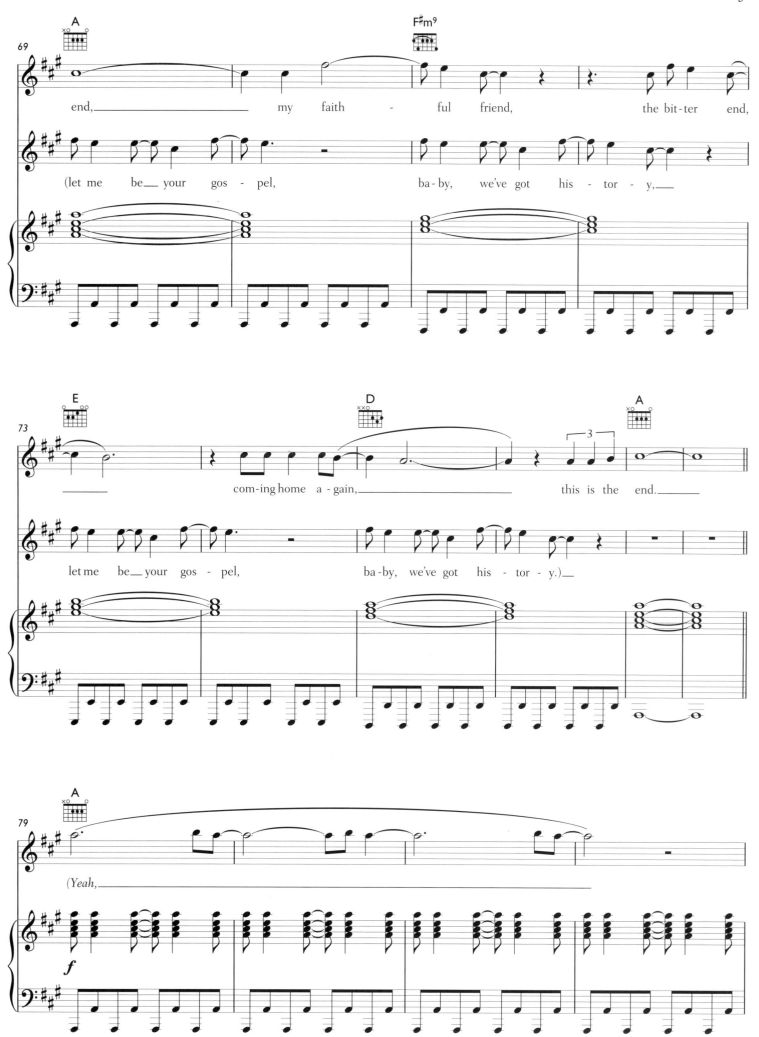

woah.)

Drink to you,__ you al - ways wished__ me well_____ and those

__ that don't,_____ go fuck__ your - self._____

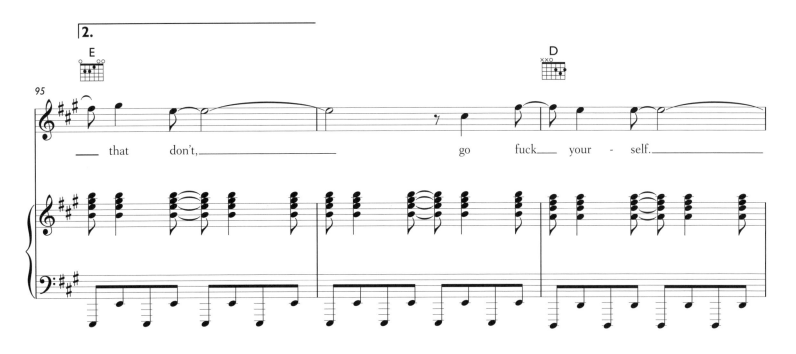

that don't,_____ go fuck____ your - self._____

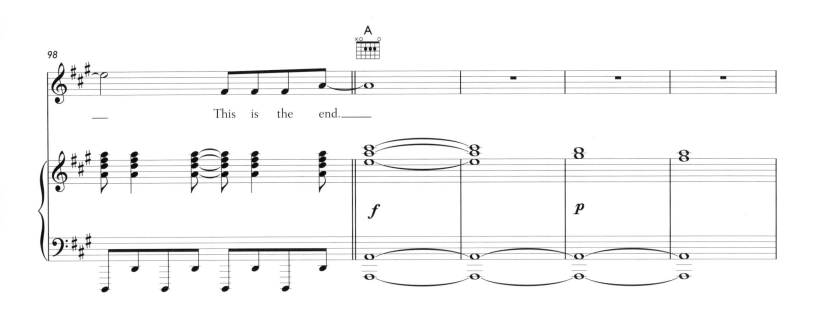

This is the end._____

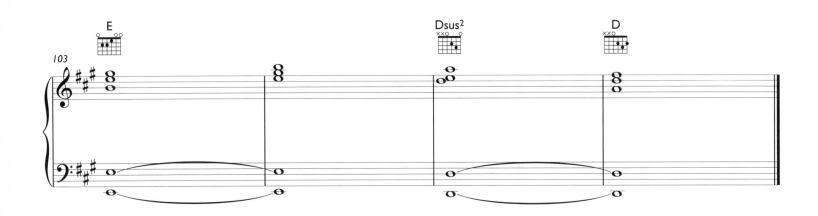

CANDY

Words and Music by Robbie Williams, Gary Barlow and Terje Olsen

1. I was there to wit - ness Can - di - ce's in - ner busi - ness, she wants the boys to no - tice_ her
2. Ring a ring of ro - ses,_ who - e - ver gets the clo - sest,_ she comes_ and she goes as_ the

rain - bows and her pon - ies._ She was e - du - cat - ed_ but could not count to ten. Now she got
war_ of the ros - es._ Moth - er was a vic - tim,_ fath - er beat the sys - tem by

doing it___ for,___ what are you do-ing it___ for,___ what are you do-ing it___ for,___ what are you

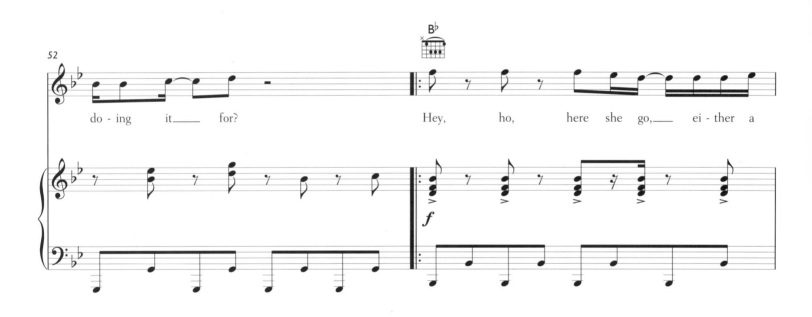

do - ing it___ for? Hey, ho, here she go,___ ei - ther a

lit - tle too high or a lit - tle too low, got no___ self - es - teem and ver - ti - go,___ cos she

DIFFERENT

Words and Music by Robbie Williams, Gary Barlow and Jacknife Lee

SHIT ON THE RADIO

Words and Music by Robbie Williams, Tim Metcalfe, Flynn Francis and Jacknife Lee

I know that you know when we get to-geth-er, love you like a hur-ri - cane,

I know that you know when we get to-geth-er, love you like a hur-ri - cane.

(Sing small notes 2° only)

(I know that you know when we get to-geth-er, love you like a hur-ri - cane,

to the shit that's on the ra-di-o, shit that's on the ra-di-o,

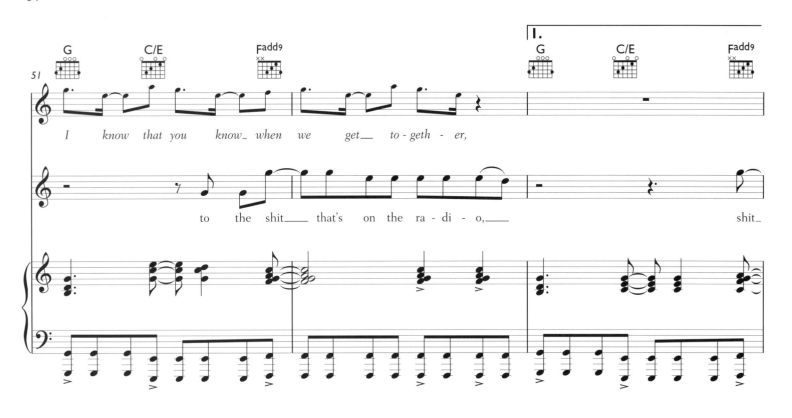

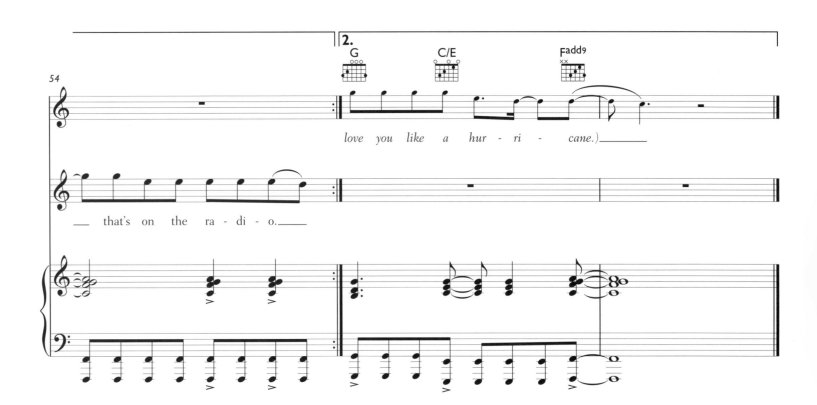

ALL THAT I WANT

Words and Music by Robbie Williams, Tim Metcalfe and Flynn Francis

HUNTING FOR YOU

Words and Music by Robbie Williams, Tim Metcalfe, Flynn Francis and Jacknife Lee

1. I walk a-round these emp-ty streets, they say there's noth-ing left for me, I say there's no-one here for you.

2. The stone is set, the dye is cast, I am the wreck-age of my past, and I am not af-raid to ask.

Down in the land, the land of the blind, the one-eyed king, he stole my

I sail a-way my san-i-ty, just to find some com-pan-

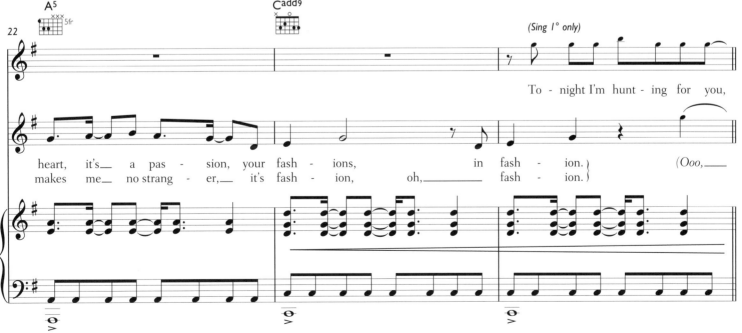

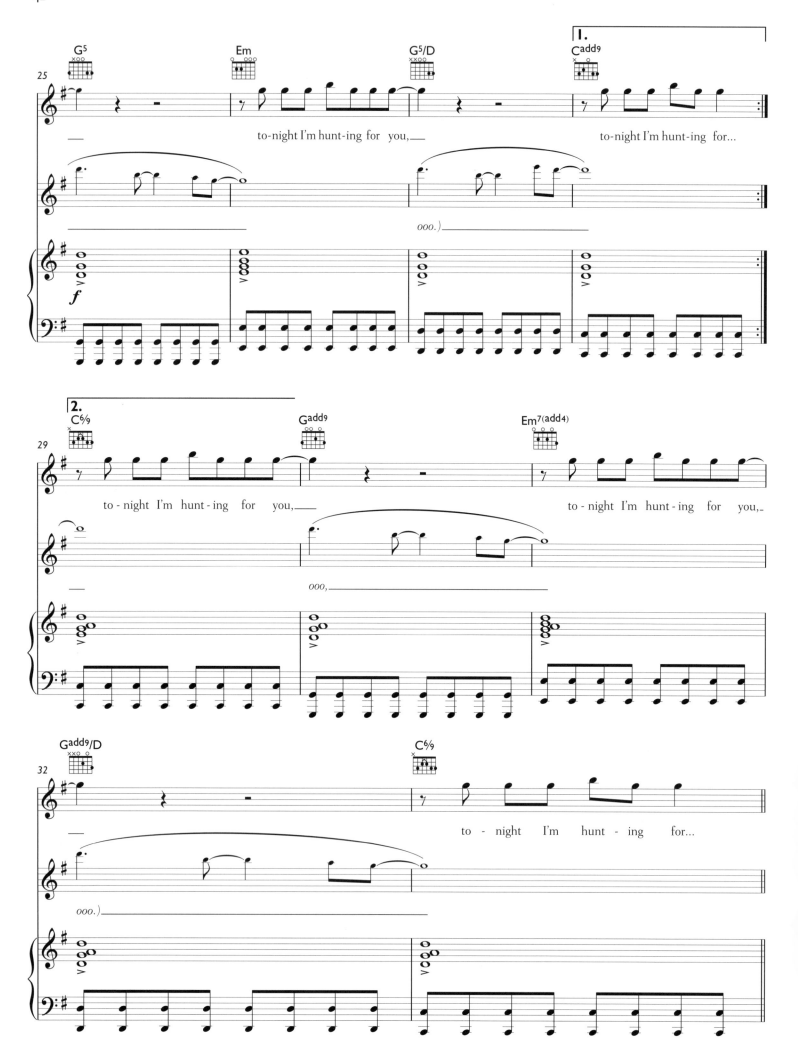

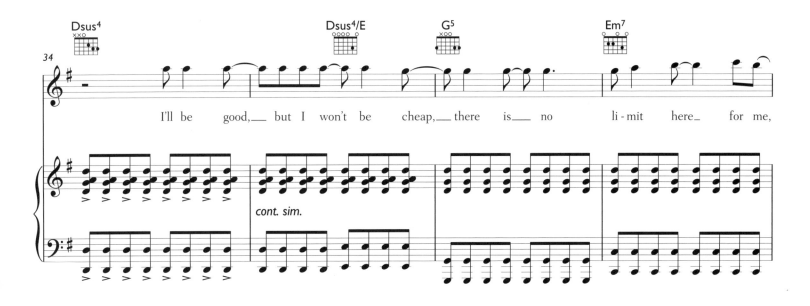

I'll be good,__ but I won't be cheap,__ there is__ no li-mit here__ for me,

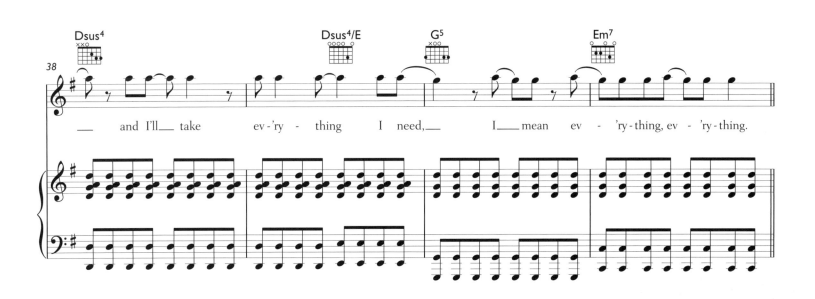

__ and I'll__ take ev-'ry-thing I need,__ I__ mean ev-'ry-thing, ev-'ry-thing.

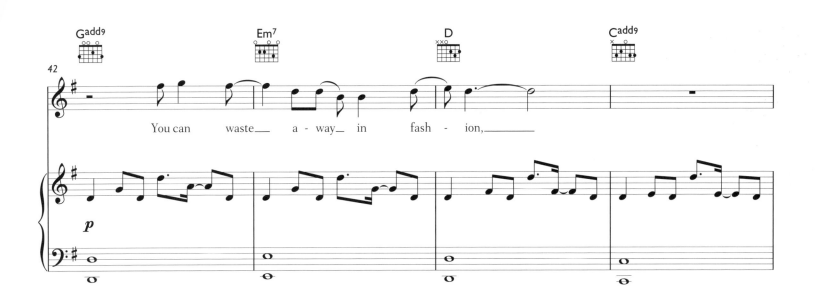

You can waste__ a-way__ in fash - ion,_____

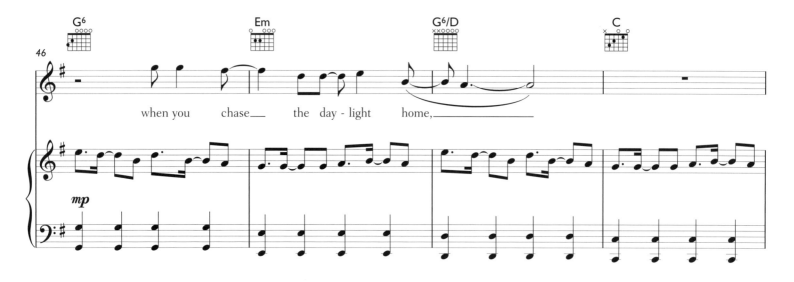

when you chase the day-light home,

you can waste a-way in fash - ion

when you chase the day-light home. To-night I'm hunt-ing for you,

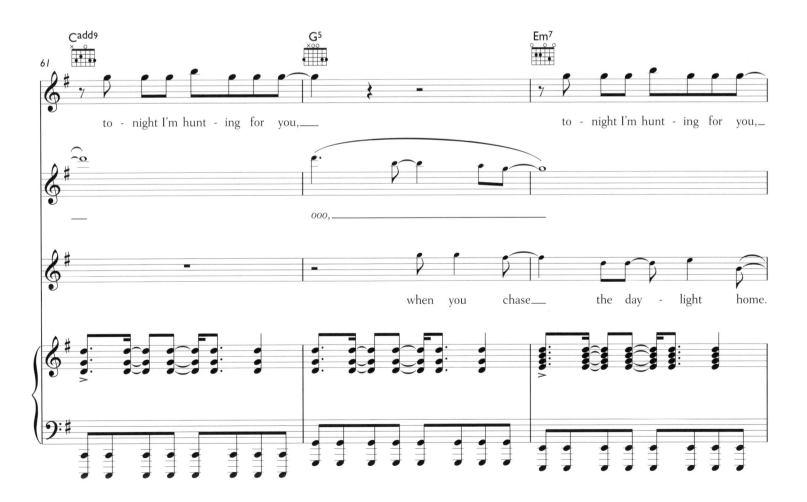

to - night I'm hunt - ing for...　　to - night I'm hunt - ing for　you.

ooo.)

INTO THE SILENCE

Words and Music by Robbie Williams, Tim Metcalfe and Flynn Francis

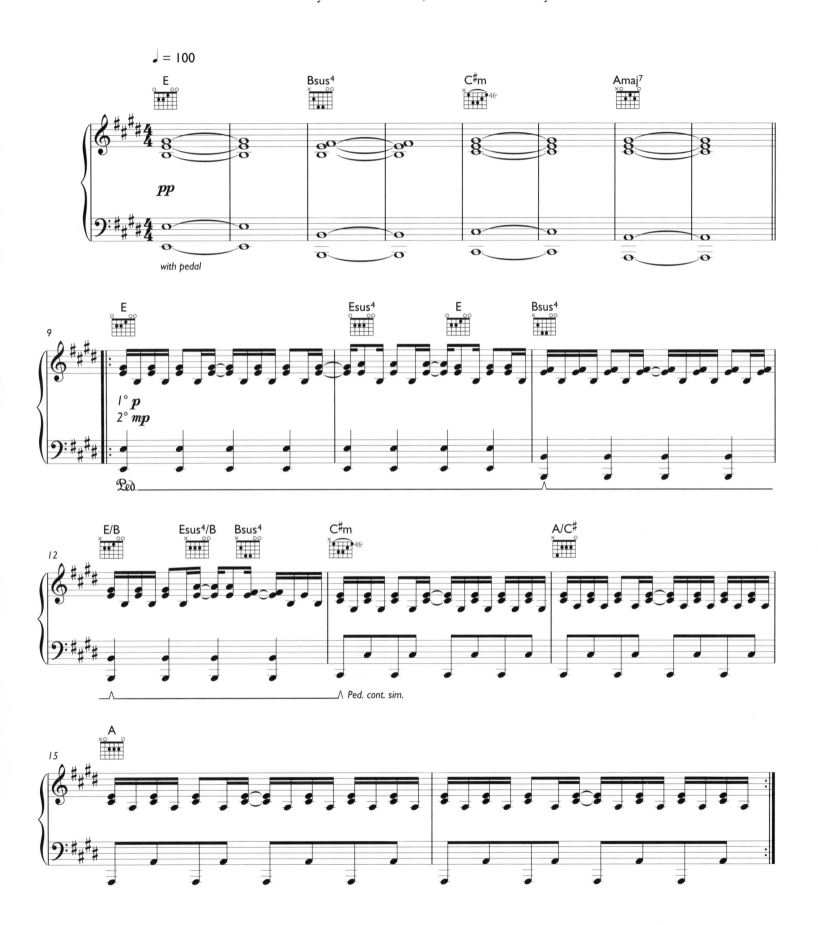

HEY WOW YEAH YEAH

Words and Music by Robbie Williams and Boots Ottestad

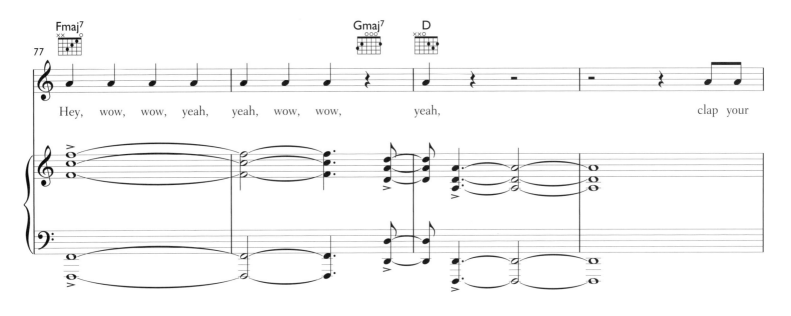

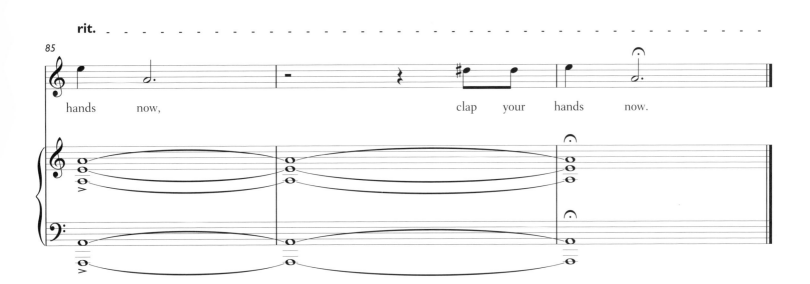

NOT LIKE THE OTHERS

Words and Music by Robbie Williams, Tim Metcalfe and Flynn Francis

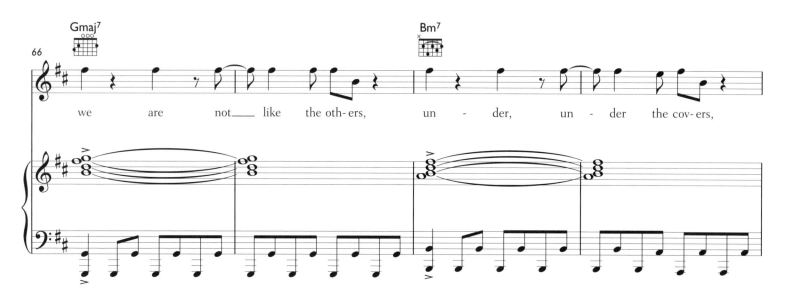

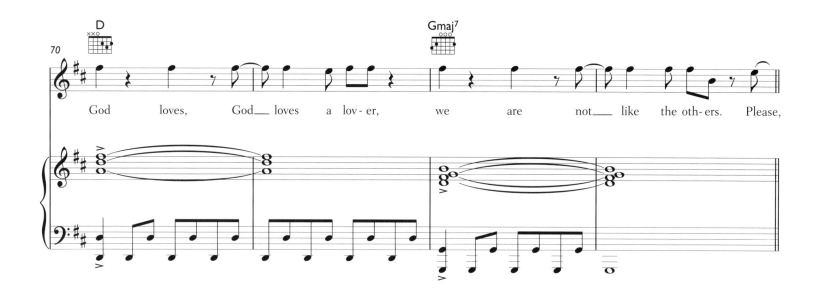

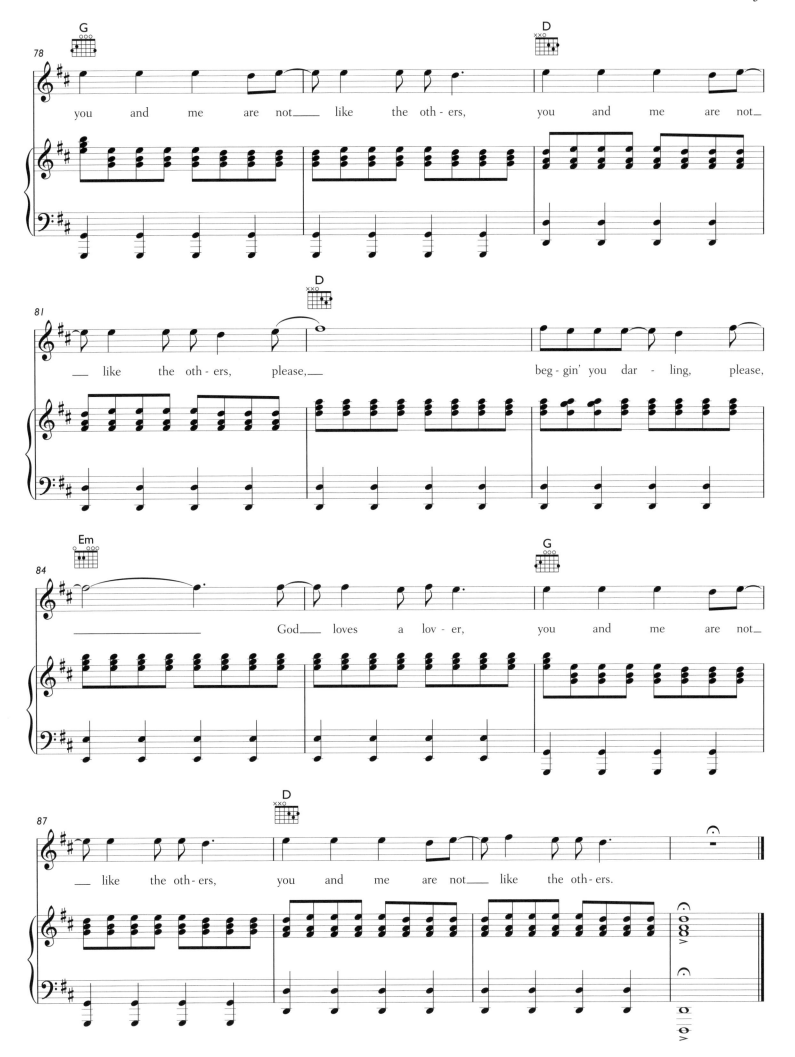

LOSERS

Words and Music by Barbara Gruska and Ethan Gruska

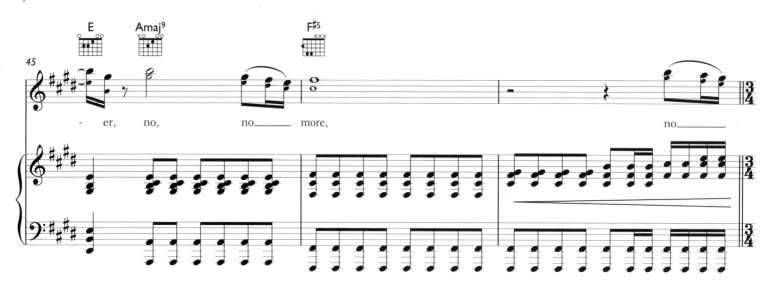

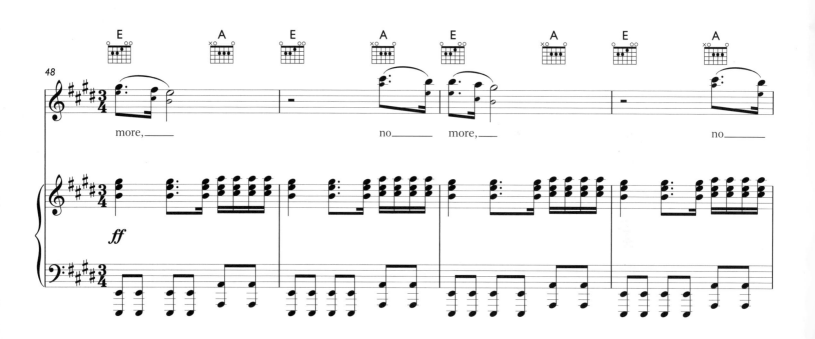